We are fostering

CW00430879

Please paste a picture
of yourself here

WELCOME

Kindercare Fostering
a specialist fostering service

Thank you to Kindercare Fostering for their kind support of this book

BAAF
ADOPTION
& FOSTERING

Published by
British Association for Adoption & Fostering (BAAF)
Skyline House
200 Union Street
London SE1 0LX
www.baaf.org.uk

© Jean Camis 2003

Charity registration 275689

ISBN 1 903699 43 6

British Library Cataloguing in Publication Data
A catalogue record for this book is available from the British Library

Editorial project management by Shaila Shah, BAAF
Designed by Andrew Haig & Associates
Typeset by Jonathan Harley
Cover illustration by Malcolm Kemp
Printed by The Lavenham Press

Contents

I would first like to thank the many children whom I have met and with whom I have worked when I was working with foster carers. Their ability to welcome children into the family, share with them, have lots of fun and games (and the occasional fight!) played a big part in inspiring this book. A big thank you also to the foster parents, without whose time, enthusiasm and commitment, fostering wouldn't happen.

I am grateful to all the people who have, in some way, helped or contributed to this book. Thanks to Tom Cairns and Hedi Argent for their initial reading of the script and their valuable comments. Thank you also to Shaila Shah, Director of Publications at BAAF, who has been dynamic in her approach and enthusiastic about the book. Thanks to Jo Francis from BAAF's Publications Department for helping to check the script and the proofs, and thanks to Hedi Argent for also drafting the guidelines.

It has been a pleasure to work with BAAF, and I thank them for making this book possible.

Jean Camis, October 2003

Children foster too!

Children whose parents foster other people's children will meet many people who are strangers to them and who come into their homes and into their lives. They will need to know and understand who they are and why they are there. The same applies with regards to the children coming to stay – who are they and why are they coming to stay? And what will it mean for your child? It is natural for foster families to give a great deal of attention to the children who come to stay. Occasionally, adults who look after other people's children and who are already parents themselves may unconsciously expect their own children to become carers too, without giving it much thought.

Although it is true to say that there is no such thing as the "perfect" parent or carer, one thing we can be certain of is that children only grow up once. Thinking about the way to talk to children about their own thoughts and feelings about fostering a child is important. Children need to know what is happening and also need to be reassured of their own position in the household and that they are loved. They may have anxieties and may worry. It is also not always as easy or as simple as a parent may think. Children often respond in ways or ask questions that adults are not prepared for.

Some years ago, I worked in a family placement team. I had considerable experience in assessing foster carers for children. I had always believed that the information I shared with the families and their children was thorough. I involved the children in discussions relevant to them and provided ample opportunity during many of my visits to continue these discussions and answer any questions, either about the fostering videos they had watched or about any concerns that they had.

Shortly after the first child had been placed with one particular foster family and towards the end of one of my visits, one of the birth children of this foster family asked if he could see me for a moment on his own. After checking with his parents that they felt comfortable with this, the boy, aged ten, asked me directly, 'When are me and my sister going to be looked after?' I felt the blood drain as I realised how frightened he must have been and what I had got wrong. I had simply not checked his understanding of the situation. This also raised the issue that, although I could assure the boy that it was highly unlikely that he or his sister would ever need to be "looked after", neither his parents nor I could guarantee that this would never happen. Interestingly, his parents were equally shocked that they had not been aware of what one of their children had been thinking for the past few weeks. It is out of my own thinking and learning from this experience that I came to write this book. I therefore dedicate it to Ian, the ten-year-old boy who asked me the question.

Jean Camis
October 2003

About this book

We are Fostering is a book for children who are involved in looking after other people's children, that is, fostering, and can also be adapted for those children who are involved in caring for a child who has been adopted into their family. I hope that the book will offer the following:

- an opportunity for children who foster – or adopt – to explore and record how they feel

- a work tool for social workers supporting children who foster or adopt

- a prompt that will promote discussions in the child's own family

- a chance to ensure that the carers' children are included from beginning to end

- a reminder that support should always be available for each individual child who fosters or adopts, no matter how long they have been carers

- a chance to look at ways in which a child who fosters or adopts may feel more confident or able to ask for help when things are going wrong, or when they feel left out, or when they feel unhappy or sad

- a chance to look at the separation and loss issues that children who foster experience

- a chance to explore how fostering and adoption affects their relationship with their own family and other extended members of their family

- a journal of memories

- a record of who stayed with them and why, and the reasons why they left and where they went

- the same opportunities as the children they help to look after of having someone independent to talk to

We are Fostering follows a questionnaire method. Each section asks both factual and open-ended questions with the aim of exploring feelings about certain issues while encouraging and reassuring the child that they have someone to talk to about the things which are important to them.

Getting started

We are Fostering is a workbook that can be used either before, during, or at any time after assessment to become a foster family.

Throughout the assessment process, your family's wishes and aspirations about looking after another child will be explored by a social worker. It is therefore important that your own child or children have the time and opportunity to think and reflect on some of the issues which may not be so clearly apparent to them. *We are Fostering* will help them to identify people in their life whom they will be able to talk to about their own feelings and experiences.

Before you give the book to your child, you should familiarise yourself with the contents. It would also be a good idea to discuss the use of this book with the social worker who is either assessing you or who supports you. If you are a social worker, it would be advisable to discuss using this book with your supervisor and, of course, with the child's parents.

Who should help your child with the completion of this workbook

This book has primarily been designed to help the child's parent(s) to work with their child or children, but does sometimes require the social worker to be included for more delicate and sensitive tasks.

The book should facilitate communication between the child, their family and the support services. There is no set way of using the book so it is left to you, the adult and the child or young person, to discuss how you wish to use it. However, there are some important points to consider.

- Set time aside when you know your child will be happy to look at the book with you. Children should feel that they are completing the book by choice and because they want to, rather than comparing it to a compulsory homework task.

- Be clear about your own views and opinions of each section of the book beforehand. Check out anything that you do not understand or feel concerned about with a social worker or another person who you know is experienced in this field.

- Try not to have any preconceived ideas about the things your child or children will bring up about any of the topics.

- Always check out things that your child has said or written that you are not clear about, so that they are not misunderstood. Let the child set the pace; no chapter or section needs to be completed in full at any one stage.

- Once the book has been started, try to see it through to the end. If your child decides that he or she wants a period of time without the book, agree to resume it later.

- Ensure you always have a genuine interest. Although this may be your intention, busy lives and other responsibilities and tasks can often get in the way of giving attention and listening.

- If you are going to use this book with more than one of your own children, it is vital that they each child has his or her own copy, and that you spend time with each child individually. Some sections can be completed jointly, and children may enjoy working on their books together for some of the time.

- Make sure that new ideas are discussed in a way that your child will understand. You may have to leave some sections of the book until your child is older.

- Be patient. This will help you to pick up important clues about what your child may be trying to express. This may be very different from your own thoughts and feelings.

- Be open and honest when your child is asking questions and trying to make sense of their own thoughts and feelings.

- Be sympathetic and supportive of your child's views, even if different from your own.

- If at any time you feel worried or anxious about anything your child or children have said, make sure you talk to someone appropriate about this.

Respecting children's privacy

There will be opportunities to talk about and to record information about the children who have come to live with you. It is important that "looked after" children are valued and respected in the same way that you would wish your own child to be valued and respected. Recorded information must therefore maintain confidentiality. This also extends to the information regarding your own children, and permission should be sought from them prior to sharing the book with others, unless this presents either a risk to them or to a placement.

Communicating with your child

When listening to your child, remember not to impose your own views or to put words into your child's mouth.

Your role is to support and to facilitate your child's ability to express themselves. Remember not to "take over" the work to be completed. It is your child's workbook and how he or she views their own experience of fostering or adopting.

Each child's experience is unique and it will be crucial for your child to get to grips with their own personal circumstances when helping to look after other children. If your child has a learning difficulty, it will be important for you to understand how he or she connects with certain situations. It may be necessary to use your child's own particular forms of communication so that he or she can make optimum use of the book. There may be parts of the book that you decide are unsuitable or you may choose to ask for assistance from someone knowledgeable about the issues and who can communicate effectively with your child.

The children with whom you can use this book

This workbook has been designed to be used with children who help to look after other children. Although it focuses on children who foster and adopt, it can also be used with children who inherit stepbrothers or sisters.

Specific guidelines on how to approach the sections in this book are provided in a separate document inserted in the pocket at the back of this book.

1

Things I know about myself

2 Things I know about myself

About me

Before you look at how you and your family become a foster family, write down some of the things that you know about you and your family.

This is a photograph of me

This photograph was taken by _____ on _____

I like this photograph because _____

_____

_____

This is a copy of my birth/adoption certificate.

My full name is
_____

I was born on
_____

On my next birthday I will be   years old
_____

My nationality is
_____

My religion is
_____

My favourite toy when I was small was
_____

My favourite toy now is
_____

This is because
_____

_____

_____

_____

My favourite story when I was small was
_____

My favourite story/book at the moment is
_____

This is because
_____

My favourite TV programme/film is
_____

This is because
_____

_____

_____

_____

My favourite song is
_____

I like this song because
_____

Other music and pop stars I like are
_____

_____

Activities and hobbies and games I enjoy are

● _____

● _____

● _____

● _____

Clubs I attend and places I visit

● _____

● _____

● _____

● _____

Things I liked about myself when I was small
_____

_____

Things I like about myself now
_____

_____

Things that make me sad

_____

Things that make me angry

_____

Things that make me happy

_____

My friends

My favourite friends are

_____

_____

The places I usually see or meet them

_____

_____

Things we usually do together

_____

_____

Something I would like to say about my friends

_____

_____

Friends are important to me because

_____

_____

6   Things I know about myself

This is a photograph of me and my friends

This photograph was taken by   on
_____

The people in the photograph are
_____
_____

The nationalities of my friends in the photograph are
_____
_____

The name of the place the photograph was taken is
_____
_____

My health

It is always helpful to know about your health.

Sadly, many children who are fostered or adopted may not get a chance to find out from their parents about their health. Look at the questions below with your parents or other members of your family to see what you can find out about your health.

Write down some things about

My teeth
_____

My eyes
_____

My skin
_____

My hair
_____

What injections did you have when you were smaller (these are sometimes called inoculations)?

_____

_____

Can you find out when you had these and where?

_____

_____

Illnesses I had when I was small

_____

_____

_____

_____

Illnesses some of my family have had and when

_____

_____

_____

_____

Can you find out if you have any allergies?

_____

_____

_____

This is what happens to me when I have an allergic reaction

_____

_____

_____

_____

My health now is generally

_____

_____

Sometimes I am not well, and this is because

_____

_____

_____

Do you take any medicines or any treatment to keep you well?

_____

_____

Do you remember any others in the past?

_____

_____

_____

_____

Is there anything else that you know about your health?

_____

_____

_____

_____

_____

_____

_____

_____

_____

_____

_____

My school

Children sometimes have to change the school they go to.

Sometimes this is because they have grown too old to continue at the same school. Sometimes children have to move schools for other reasons. This could be because they have moved with their family to another home in a different area.

Sometimes children who will stay with you will have to change their school because their old school is too far away from where they live now.

What does school mean to you?

The school I go to now is called
_____

The address is
_____

_____

This is a photograph of my school

Things I would like to say about my school

_____

_____

_____

The school I went to before this one was called

_____

Things I would like to say about the school(s) I used to go to

_____

_____

_____

The subjects I study at school

_____

_____

The subjects I like most are

_____

_____

The subjects I find difficult are

_____

_____

The things that I am good at in school are

_____

_____

12 Things I know about myself

Something nice I have done at school is

_____

_____

Things I do in the playground at break times

_____

_____

How I get to school

_____

_____

How I get home

_____

_____

Things I would miss about my school now if I left

_____

_____

Other things I'd like to say about school

_____

_____

_____

Things I hope to do when I am grown up and leave school

_____

_____

Date
_____

Things I would like to remember about my school

This page is for you to stick in any certificates you have received, stories you have written or drawings from school that you may like to keep with this book.

What happens to children who have to change schools?

Let's look at some of the things that happen to children who have to change schools because their old school is too far away.

They may have to change their school because it is too far to travel

If they have to change schools, they will have to say goodbye to their friends

Learning can be difficult

Making new friends can be difficult

Changing schools might make them feel angry, sad or lonely

Being at school might remind them of when they lived at home

They may have had a teacher they liked at their last school or someone they could talk to and they may miss them

2 My family and what we are like

Different families

Families come in all shapes, sizes and colours. In some there are two parents and in some there is one. Some families have many family members and some have just a few. Some have lots of children and others don't. Some families include very close friends or people who are not directly related but who are seen as part of the family. Look at the pictures of the different families below to see which one looks most like your family.

Posed by models. John Birdsall Photography

Posed by models. John Birdsall Photography

DigitalVision

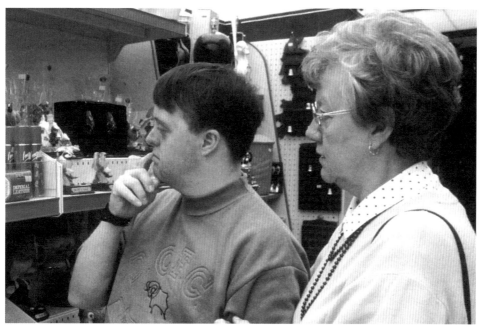

Posed by models. John Birdsall Photography except where indicated

Who's who in your family

This is a photograph of me and my family

The people in this photograph are

_____

_____

_____

_____

This photograph was taken by

_____

on

_____

The place was

_____

Date _____

20 My family

My mother's nationality is

She was born in

My mother's religion is

My father's nationality is

He was born in

My father's religion is

My brother(s)' and sister(s)' nationality is

My grandparent's nationality is

My grandparent's religion is

I have   step parent(s)

Their names are

Other people who are important to me and the places they come from

Date

Brothers and sisters

Have you got any brothers or sisters? Remember to include step, half and adopted brothers and sisters. If you have, write down their names and when they were born in the spaces below. Or stick photographs of them in the spaces or draw their faces.

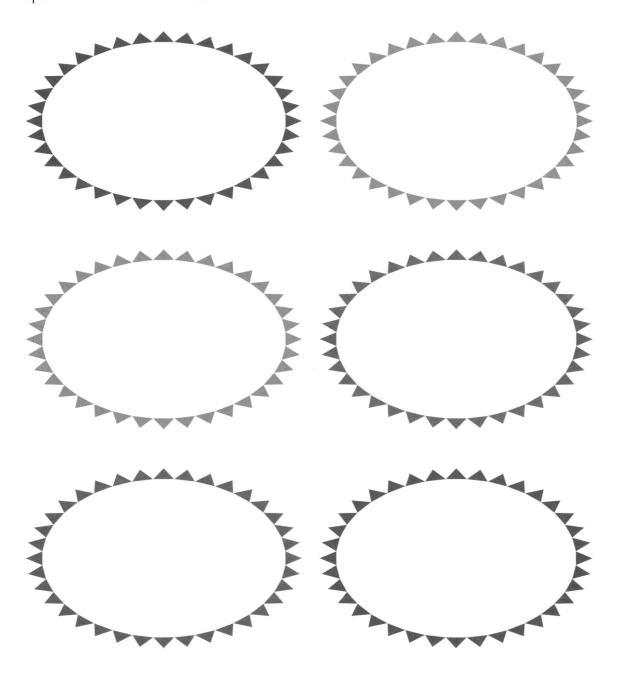

Perhaps you have more brothers and sisters than can fit into the spaces above. If so, use another sheet or get them to share spaces.

If you do not have this many brothers or sisters, include cousins or use the space in any way you like.

A picture of your family

In the space below, draw a picture of your family starting with the oldest at the top, going from left to right, to the youngest at the bottom right! If your family is too big to fit into the space below, draw their faces and write their ages underneath.

Their names are

Date

Other people in your family

Use this page to stick photographs of other members of your family who live in the same house as you. This may include brothers and sisters, cousins, aunties and uncles, grandparents or someone who has become a member of your family. Being part of a family does not necessarily mean that a person has to be directly related to you. Sometimes a close family friend may become a part of your family. You may even want to include a family pet!

This page is for you to draw or write about family members who do not live in the same house as you or people who, although not directly related, have become a close member of your family.

Don't forget to write down their names and who they are!

How important is your family to you? Let's find out!

Something I would like to say about my family

This is what my family means to me

Things that we enjoy doing together as a family are

These are the times when I most need my family

These are some of the things that make me and my family look alike

Date

Where you live

This is a photograph/drawing of where we live

I have lived here with my family since

The address of my home is

Things I like about living here are

Things I don't like about living here are

Places I like to visit near by are

Being away from your family

Sometimes, for many different reasons, children may have to move away from their family for a while.

How would you feel if this happened to you?

Think about a time when you have been away from your family and how that made you feel. For instance, it may have been your first day at school, or you may have stayed at a friend's house for a sleepover, or gone on a school trip or had to stay in hospital. Below, write down some of the thoughts and feelings that you had when you had to spend a short time away from your family. Maybe you felt excited...maybe you felt sad and frightened.

_____

_____

_____

_____

_____

_____

_____

_____

_____

_____

Date _____

What happens to children who have to move?

Let's look at some of the things that happen to children who move away from home and their family.

They will be separated from their parent/s

They may have to leave brothers or sisters behind

They may have to change schools

They will miss playing with their friends

They will feel worried about being in a new school

They won't have familiar things around them

They will have to get used to a new house

Can you think of other things? Write them in the spaces below.

Family talk

Who in your family would you talk to if you were unhappy, angry, sad, or had something really exciting to tell?

Write down their names in the spaces below and the reason why you would choose that particular person to talk to.

Name	Name
I would choose this person because	I would choose this person because

Name	Name
I would choose this person because	I would choose this person because

You can tell people things in different ways

Children can talk to grown-ups about their feelings. These may be happy feelings they want to share or times when they are feeling sad or upset about something.

Grown-ups will talk to children to help them to learn different things as they grow up and teach them how to be safe.

Sometimes children and grown-ups will use sign language or other ways of talking to each other.

It is also important to stop and listen to what the other person has to say.

Sometimes children will be able to say things better in another language.

Sometimes grown-ups will only talk to other grown-ups about things they have to say.

Drawing a picture of something you have seen or a face of how you feel is also a way of telling a grown-up the things that you are thinking or feeling.

Sometimes it is easier to write down the words that are difficult to say.

Sometimes children whisper or tell secrets to other children. Sometimes a grown-up may tell a child a secret. The secret about secrets is that they should be shared with someone you can talk to in your family.

Who else can you talk to?

There might be specific problems that you need or want to talk to someone about, once you have children come to live with you. Think about the different people to whom you can ask some questions and get some answers. Ask the social worker who visits you and your family to have a look at this page with you before you fill it in. You could ask them to help you if you like.

If my foster brother or sister tells me something that worries me, I will tell …

_____

If someone hurts me I will tell …

_____

If I get blamed for something I haven't done, I will talk to …

_____

When I am angry with my family, I will talk to …

_____

When things don't seem fair, I will talk to …

_____

This is what I can do if I don't feel I am being listened to

_____

_____

_____

_____

What else might you want to talk to your family about? And who would you want to tell? Write the answers in the shapes below.

Family ways

Family ways are important. Every family has a different way of living together. Sometimes the way in which a mum or dad will bring up their children is because their parents (your grandparents) used the same ways. Ask your mum or dad if there is anything that they do today that their parents did many years ago when bringing them up. This might be making sure that everyone sits at a table to eat or has to leave their shoes at the front door before coming into the house.

Use the boxes below to write down some of the rules in your home and some of the things that you like to do as a family sharing the same home.

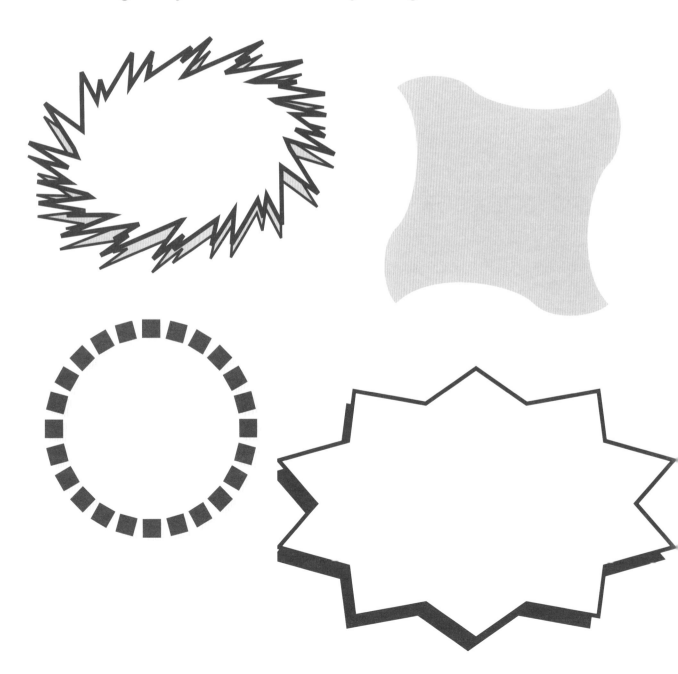

Different family ways

Children who come to live with you when you are being a foster family may have been used to different family ways. What other things do you think they may be used to doing in their home that are different to the things that you do?

- _____
- _____
- _____
- _____
- _____
- _____
- _____
- _____
- _____

Other things I would like to say about this

_____

_____

_____

_____

_____

_____

_____

What kind of things can you do to help children who come to stay with you?

Try to think of ways that will help them to get to know you and to understand the family ways in your home

Some things that I think will be important to other children visiting my home are

Celebrations!

What kind of things do you and your family celebrate during the year?
Why don't you make up a calendar of special days and events below?

January	
February	
March	
April	
May	
June	
July	
August	
September	
October	
November	
December	

During any year, there are many other celebrations that take place, some in this country and some in other countries. Because everyone and every family is different, not all families will celebrate the same occasions or special events. Find out what other events are celebrated during the year which are different to the ones celebrated by your family.

The date

Name of celebration

Other information about this

The date

Name of celebration

Other information about this

The date

Name of celebration

Other information about this

The date

Name of celebration

Other information about this

3 Sharing and what this means

Sharing

Do you remember what things you thought about when we looked at family ways?

Did you and your family think about sharing? Sometimes families share things without even knowing that they're doing it! Write down some of the things you and your family share together. This may be a thing like the telephone, the TV, a bedroom, a bathroom, books, games, photographs or it could be telling stories or giving lots of hugs.

- _____
- _____
- _____
- _____
- _____
- _____
- _____
- _____
- _____

Things I would like to say about this

_____

_____

_____

_____

_____

_____

Sharing your parents

Sharing your parents with anybody, even a brother or sister, can be difficult! There will be times when you want time and attention all for yourself, and you may feel upset if you can't have it. Have you had these feelings? The answer is probably Yes! Before we look at why sharing can be difficult, here are some things to think about.

- How do you think a child who comes to live with you might feel about having to leave his or her own parents?

_____

_____

_____

_____

_____

- How would you feel about sharing your parent or parents with a child who comes to live with you, and what would help you do this?

_____

_____

_____

_____

- What do you think the difficulties and problems could be?

_____

_____

_____

_____

Here is some information that might help you

Children who have to leave their parents and their home will feel sad, upset or even angry about having to leave. They will feel worried about where they are going to go, what sort of place they will live in and what kind of foster family they will have. They may wonder what the children in the foster family will be like. Will the new foster carers be nice to them and look after them well, and keep them safe? Will the children in the new home be friendly and play with them, or not? It will be important for you, as a family member, to welcome the child into your home. Remember that the child coming to live with you will have lots of muddled feelings and will probably feel anxious about being in a strange family with all these new people.

Rules

Every family and home has different rules, and every parent has a different way of doing things. The child coming to live with you will have to follow the rules that your parents have but, in some cases, your parents may make different rules for the new child. This may seem strange to you at first, but there will be good reasons for this. For example, it may be that if you break something in your house, your parents will tell you off, or shout at you or send you to your room. Or they may tell you not to worry, and say that these sorts of things can happen.

For children coming to stay with you, hearing an adult shout at them may make them feel very afraid. It may remind them of when their parents shouted at them and even hit them if they had done something wrong. Your parents may treat a foster child differently and not shout, but be kind and understanding in a way they aren't always with you! But remember that your parents will have been trained to be foster carers for children who have had bad experiences at home, and so they will know how to deal with them without making them afraid.

Sometimes, some children who want attention from other people may break or damage things on purpose. Or they may say something which is upsetting, and get away with it. You may wonder why they are not getting a telling off, as you would! This may be difficult for you to understand at times, so it is important that you talk to someone about how you feel. So if you are feeling unhappy or feeling left out, don't forget to tell your family how you feel so that they know.

Sharing your things

Sharing with a child that comes to live with you will not just be about sharing your parents and their time, love and attention. It will also mean sharing your toys, your games, and things in your house.

Sometimes you may not want to share something with a child who comes to stay. Sometimes children will take things that do not belong to them. If this happens to you, it may make you feel angry or upset. But it can also be fun to share! You could play with your toys together, and having another child to come and live with you will mean one more person to play games with! Think about how you could help the child join in.

Here is a little exercise for you to do. In the box below, on the left hand side, write down all the things you don't like about sharing. And then when you've finished, on the right hand side, write down all the things that you like about sharing.

What I don't like about sharing	What I like about sharing
● _____	● _____
● _____	● _____
● _____	● _____
● _____	● _____
● _____	● _____
● _____	● _____
● _____	● _____
● _____	● _____
● _____	● _____
● _____	● _____

If you found more good things than bad things about sharing, you can see that sharing can be fun!

Most children coming to stay with you will want to bring things that are important to them. What kind of things do you think that they would like to bring and why?

●
_____
●
_____
●
_____
●
_____

Do you think that they might be worried about sharing their things with you? What might worry them about sharing their things?

●
_____
●
_____
●
_____
●
_____

It is not always possible to replace things that get broken and this can be very upsetting for everyone, including other members of your family.

Can you remember breaking anything? If so, what was it and how did it happen?

_____

_____

_____

_____

What did your parent(s) say to you? Can you remember what happened?

_____

_____

_____

_____

_____

Can you remember a time when something in the household broke down? What was this? And what did you and your family have to do to fix it or replace it?

_____

_____

_____

_____

How did this make you and your family feel?

_____

_____

_____

_____

_____

_____

_____

_____

How to make sharing easier

Here is another little exercise. In the box below, on the left hand side, write down what you think could be difficult about sharing. Then, on the right hand side, write down how you could make this easier, so that the difficulties go away.

What I find difficult about sharing	How I can make sharing easier
● _____	● _____
● _____	● _____
● _____	● _____
● _____	● _____
● _____	● _____
● _____	● _____
● _____	● _____
● _____	● _____

You have probably thought of some really good ideas. Share these with your parents and the social worker who comes to visit you – they will be really impressed!

4 How we became a foster family

Why children have to live away from home

Before we look at how you and your family become a foster family, let's look at why some children cannot always live at home.

There are many reasons why some children cannot live at home with their parents. Sometimes, mums and dads can't look after their children properly because they don't know how to look after them, or they don't want to. Sometimes it's because the parents become ill and can't cope. Sometimes it's because the parents aren't getting along too well and are having lots of arguments and fights with each other, and the children may then get shouted at and may even get hit. All these things can affect children badly and make them unhappy and not do well at school.

At these times, parents will need help. They may need help to learn to become better parents and look after their children well. They may need time to get better if they are ill. They may need special help to enable them to get on with each other and with their children, and to treat their children with kindness and love.

A "social worker" from the local council will visit the family and offer them some help. The social worker may decide that it is best for the child or children in the family to be looked after by other people while their parents sort themselves out. It can be difficult for parents to accept that their child should be looked after by someone else. Some of them may not agree that their child should leave them and be looked after by other parents. Others may agree that this will be best for their child. In either case, it is the social worker's job to try to make sure that the child stays well and safe.

All this can be really difficult. Imagine what it might be like if you had lots of problems at home and you could see that your parent or parents were also having lots of problems and that you had to leave home because of this. You may feel that your parents don't love you or that they don't care about you. You may wonder why they can't try to do better. This is probably how the child who is coming to live with you feels.

Why can't someone else look after them?

Some children may be lucky. They may have other relatives who can look after them, like grandparents or aunties or uncles. Sadly, not all children have other relatives who can do this, and sometimes, those who can help look after them may not live nearby or are not always able to help out. For example, grandparents might be able to spend short periods of time with their grandchild, but might find it difficult to manage to look after them for longer periods. Aunties and uncles may have to go to work, or may not have a house that's big enough to look after another child. This does not mean that they don't care enough for the child, just that they may not be able to help look after the child properly.

Why foster families are so important

You can see now why foster families are so important. They can help out at a time when a child or a group of brothers and sisters needs a place to live when they can't live at home.

One thing is very clear and important for you to remember. The reason why a child may come to live with your family is not because something happened which was their fault. It is because their parents can't or won't look after them properly, and they need to be safe and well cared for, just like any other child.

Fostering and what this means

For a family like yours, fostering means that you have offered to look after someone else's child or children for a certain amount of time. Fostering involves everybody in the household – parents, children, and any other people who might be staying there.

Foster families have to work very hard to help the children who come to live with them to feel loved and to feel safe. They learn how to do this and once they have learnt, the council or an independent fostering agency "approves" them to be foster carers.

Sometimes a child comes to live with you because their parents have said that they can't cope and have asked for the child to be "accommodated". This means they have asked social workers to find another family for the child while they sort themselves out. At other times, a child may come to live with you because the local council has decided that it is safer and better for the child to live with your family than to continue staying at home. Sometimes a court will be involved, and will decide that a child needs a foster family. Other times, the court may decide that the child can't go back to their own family, and needs a permanent adoptive family.

Every family is different, and the social worker who visits you will talk to you and your family about the child coming to stay with you. He or she will explain why that child is coming to stay, and will give you a rough idea about how long the child will stay. The social worker will talk to you all about your own thoughts and feelings about having that particular child to stay, so you will have a chance to ask questions about anything that you are not sure of or anything that worries you.

Every foster family has the chance to say yes or no to a particular child coming to stay. This means that when the child does come to stay with you, the child will know that he or she is wanted, and that you and your family will help look after them and make them feel comfortable and welcome.

Different kinds of fostering

There are different kinds of fostering, and these are listed below.

Short-term fostering

Sometimes, foster families might agree to something called "short-term placements". This means that a child will come to stay with you for a few weeks or a few months. This will give their own parents a chance to sort themselves out so that the child can return home.

Short breaks

Sometimes a disabled child who has to have a lot of special care and attention may need a short break from home. Social workers then help find a foster family maybe for a weekend or a week. Sometimes, this may be for just a few hours at a time.

Long-term fostering

Sometimes, social workers may move children into a foster family for a longer period. This may be months or even years. This could mean that a child will stay with your family for some time, go home to his or her own parents, and then come and stay again. This might be because things have become difficult for them again at home. For the child, it is always nice to return to a family whom they know.

Sometimes, a child will have to stay for a long time because they can never go back home. They may then be adopted or they will remain as a long-term foster child.

Your social worker will come to talk to you and your family about how long the child who is coming to live with you will stay. They will want to know all your thoughts and feelings about this, and then decide what is going to be best for the child and best for you and your family.

Adoption and what this means

Adoption is different from fostering because it means that a child joins a new family forever. The child's adoptive parents become the child's legal parents by going to court. Adoption happens when it is not possible for the child to return to the birth parents.

The adoptive family is the child's family by law and is responsible for the child in every way, just as if the child was born to them. If there are other children in that family who were born to the adoptive parents, they will become the child's brothers and sisters. And their grandparents will become the child's grandparents ... and their uncles and aunts will become the child's uncles and aunts ... and it is like having a whole new family.

There are lots of books and leaflets available explaining fostering and adoption in more detail and some of these are listed at the back. You could read these with your family as well as using this book. Ask your social worker to get some for you.

In the space below, perhaps you and your family would like to make a few notes about the difference between fostering and adoption.

Fostering   **Adoption**

_____

_____

_____

_____

_____

_____

_____

_____

Preparing to be a foster family

Can you remember what you and your family talked about when you first began to think about fostering children? Where were you when this happened? Can you remember what was said?

_____

_____

_____

_____

Write down some of the reasons why you and your family have decided to look after another child or other children.

_____

_____

_____

_____

My own thoughts and feelings about this

_____

_____

_____

_____

Can you remember what sort of information you received about caring for other children? Can you remember what it said?

_____

_____

_____

_____

_____

What did you all do after you got this information?

_____

_____

_____

Write down some of the questions that you and your family want to ask or have already asked the social worker about having a child come to live with you.

- _____
- _____
- _____
- _____
- _____
- _____
- _____
- _____
- _____

The visit from the social worker

A social worker will come to talk to your family about what it will mean for all of you to foster a child. The social worker will also want to find out if your family will be the right family for the child.

Our first visit from the social worker was on
_____

The social worker's name
_____

The name of the agency that he/she works for
_____

Their work address
_____

_____

Their telephone number
_____

Things that they told us
_____

_____

_____

_____

_____

Things that they brought to show us
_____

_____

_____

_____

_____

Things that I would like to say about the visit
_____

_____

_____

_____

Other things that I would like to know are

_____

_____

_____

_____

_____

Can you think of any other things the social worker has told you?

_____

_____

_____

_____

_____

_____

Do you know if you or your parents have been invited to an information meeting about fostering along with other families?   Yes ❑   No ❑

Whether it is the social worker's first or second or third visit, you and your family may have been given a video to watch of other families who have fostered. Have you and your family seen a video yet?   Yes ❑   No ❑

If yes, write something on what you thought about the video and what you learnt.

_____

_____

_____

_____

If no, how about asking your parents to ask the social worker when he or she contacts you next? Better still, why don't you ask the social worker yourself when he or she visits next?

Looking after a child from another family – what this will mean

These are the things I would like to say about children who sometimes have to live with another family

_____

_____

_____

_____

These are the things I would like to say about how I would feel about looking after a child from another family

_____

_____

_____

These are the people to whom I will talk about this

_____

_____

_____

These are some of the things that the social worker has talked to us about

- _____
- _____
- _____
- _____
- _____

These are some of the things my family and I talked about after the social worker's visits

_____

_____

Things I would like to say about this

_____

_____

What I feel that looking after children will mean for me

_____

_____

Things that worry me about having a child come to live with us

_____

Things that I am looking forward to

_____

_____

The reasons why I think it is important for me to have someone to talk to about us becoming a foster family

_____

_____

_____

Getting approved

These are the other things my family and I have done to help us to become a foster family

- _____
- _____
- _____
- _____
- _____
- _____

These are some of the changes we have made to make it happen

- _____
- _____
- _____
- _____
- _____

Other things I would like to say about this

_____

_____

_____

_____

_____

This is what we have done to get "approved" to become a foster family

_____

_____

_____

_____

_____

_____

_____

_____

The date when we were approved was

_____

Use this page to write about or draw anything else you and your family have done to prepare to be a foster family.

This is a photograph of me and my family the week that we became a foster family

This photograph was taken by _____ on _____

How about asking the social worker if he or she would be in a photograph with you?

The date when this photograph was taken was _____

It was the social worker's _____ visit to my family.

5 Having children come to stay

Saying hello and goodbye

Let's look at saying hello and goodbye to people. Can you remember starting at your school and thinking how strange it was to meet all the new teachers and all your new classmates?

In the space below, write down some of the things you remember about this.

_____

_____

_____

_____

_____

_____

_____

Now, write down some of the feelings you had about leaving and saying goodbye to any of your friends or any teachers that you liked because you had to change schools.

_____

_____

_____

_____

_____

_____

Date _____

In the spaces below, write down other times that you have said hello and who to. This could be when you have visited friends or other members of your family or met people on holiday.

Date

In the spaces below, write down some of the happy and sad feelings about saying goodbye.

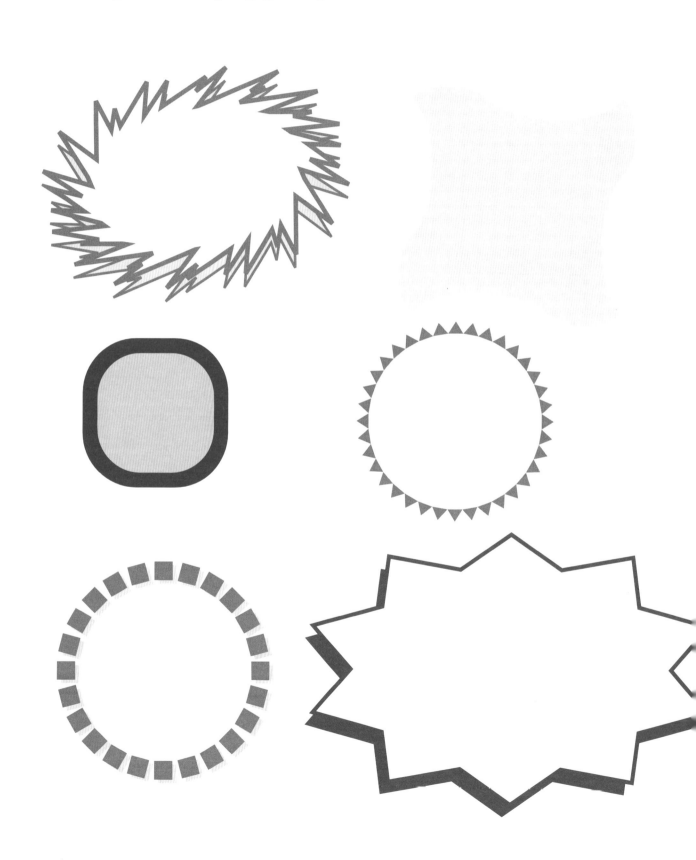

Now, in the spaces below write down how you think children who will come and stay with you will feel about saying goodbye to their parents and family, even if it's only for a short time.

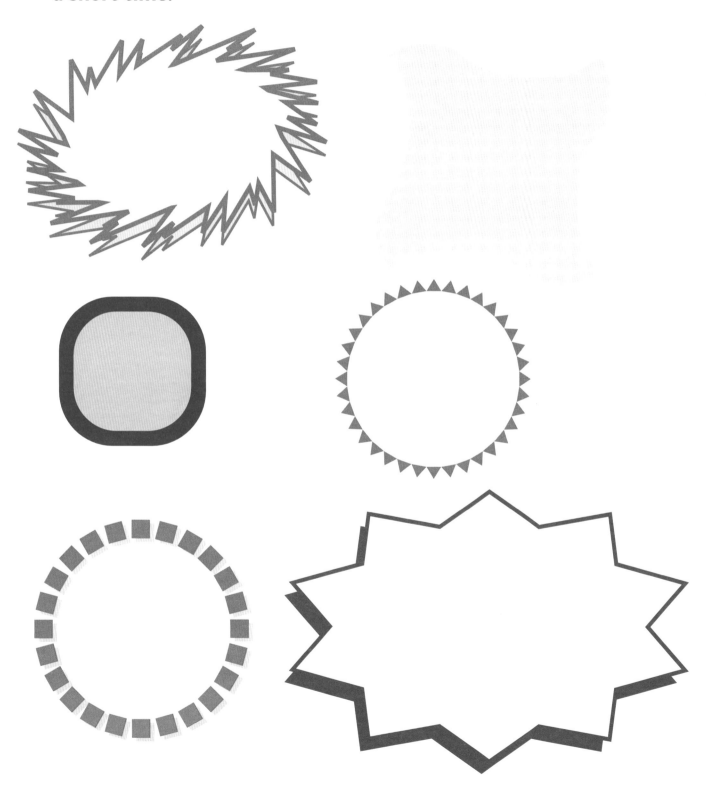

Now make a list of all the things you and your family can do to make another child feel better about coming to stay with you. Here's some examples to get you started. Perhaps you will get them to meet friends. Or you will share your toys or PlayStation with them. Or you will help them get used to how you and your family do things! What else can you think of?

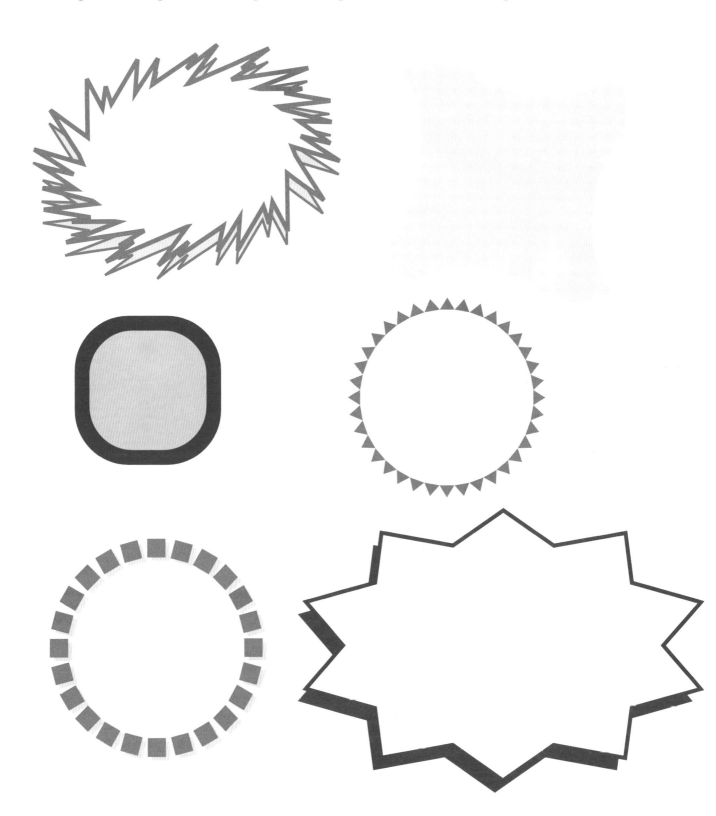

Welcoming a child

Helping a child to feel welcome in your home can be difficult for both you and the child who has come to stay. Look at some of the things you may like to think about before they arrive at your door!

These are the things that I am going to say to the child that visits my home for the first time

_____

_____

_____

_____

These are the things I think they might like to eat and drink when they arrive

_____

_____

_____

_____

These are some of the things that I am going to show them and which I am going to share with them

_____

_____

_____

_____

Things that I am going to do and say to make them feel welcome are

_____

_____

_____

_____

_____

_____

_____

_____

If the child does not want to speak to me or share my things when they first arrive I will do these things to make them feel better. I will:

● _____

● _____

● _____

● _____

● _____

● _____

● _____

● _____

● _____

● _____

● _____

● _____

My first "Hello"

If you've already had a child come to stay, when did you first say "Hello" to the child? How did this happen?

_____

_____

is the name of the first child who visited
_____

The date that _____ was born was
_____

Their first visit to our home was on _____ and they stayed for
_____

This is what I talked about

_____

_____

This is what they said

_____

_____

This is what I did

_____

_____

I did this because

_____

_____

After the visit, this is what my family talked about

_____

_____

And this is how I felt

_____

_____

The day that _____ moved in with us was
_____
The date was _____ and the time was
_____
Our first meal together was
_____
This is where we had our meal
_____

Things that _____ said to me and my family were

_____

Something nice I said to _____ was

_____

Something of mine that I said _____ could share with me was

_____

Something of theirs that I liked was

_____

When the child first moves in

This is how I felt after they had moved in

_____

_____

_____

_____

Things me and my family talked about were

_____

_____

_____

_____

This is how long   might stay with us for

_____

It may make you sad to think about this, but sometimes some children who come to stay with you will not be able to remember some things about their own family. This is why their social worker and your family may try to get information about the child and their family so that it can be kept for them in a book. This is called a life story book and will have photos and information about their family story.

Perhaps you could have some photos taken of you and the child who is staying with you so they can also put the photos in their book. This will help them to remember you when they leave. And putting some of the photos in this book – which is YOUR book – will help you to remember them when they have gone.

What about choosing a photograph now that you can both put in your books? How about choosing this together?

This is a photograph of
_____

This photo was taken on   at
_____

Things that we both like are

_____

Things that we both dislike are

_____

Things that we like to do together are

_____

Things that we do differently are

_____

On this page, you can write anything else you feel about the child who has come to stay. You might choose to draw a picture, write a story, add more photographs, or write down what has happened, what you have learnt or how you feel. The choice is yours!

Making changes

Before another child or children come to stay, there are many things that need to happen. Sometimes this means that you and your family have to make changes in your home. Can you think of any thing that you or your family has had to do before a child has come to stay, to make it better for that child or to make it safe for them?

_____

_____

_____

_____

_____

_____

_____

This is how I felt about some of these changes

_____

_____

_____

_____

_____

_____

_____

Saying "goodbye"

Foster placements come to an end for many different reasons.

Generally, it's because a child will leave your home to go back to live with their family. Or a child may move on to live with a different foster family or an adoptive family.

Sometimes moves happen so quickly that there is not enough time to say all the things you would like to. Children who move away suddenly might cause you and the rest of your family to have all sorts of feelings. This can be very upsetting.

Saying "goodbye" can be OK when you are saying "goodbye" to a friend or a relative because you know you can look forward to the next time that you are going to see them.

But saying "goodbye" to a child you and your family have looked after is different. This is because you know the child is going home to their family and you may not know if you will see them again. You and your family may have lots of different feelings about this. You may feel very happy for the child because you know this is the right thing to happen, even though you will miss them.

You might not feel very happy about them going home; if you feel anxious about how they will get on, it is important that you talk to someone about it.

Sometimes you might feel very pleased that a child has left because finally you can have some peace and quiet! Whatever your feelings about saying "goodbye", it is always good to know that you have someone to talk to.

It is nice to do something special before a child who has stayed with you moves on. This might be having a favourite tea or dinner or going out. You might like to draw them a picture or write something to give to them. Or give a little present that you know they would like.

It is always a good feeling to know that you have done something nice to help another child, who has stayed with you, to say "goodbye" even if you did not really want him or her to go. Remember, it may be as hard for the foster child to say "goodbye" as it is for you.

My first "goodbye"

Fill in the spaces below to show how you feel about having said "goodbye"

This is a drawing of my face and how I feel today

This is a drawing of my face and how I looked when they left

Other thoughts and feelings about saying goodbye

_____

_____

_____

_____

_____

_____

_____

Date
_____

Do children still see their own parents and families when they live with us?

Most of the children who come to stay with you will see their own parents or other people from their family from time to time. Some of the children may not, but may receive letters or celebration cards or gifts.

Sometimes the parents may come to your house to visit their child and sometimes your parents may be asked to take the child or children to another place to see their parents or other members of their family like sisters or brothers or grandparents.

Although you may be thinking that the children will be happy after seeing their parents, this is not always so. Sometimes they have very different feelings and may be angry or upset or sad. They may need some time on their own afterwards.

Others may need to talk to someone, and that person could be you.

It is always important for you to talk to someone about things that other children who are staying have said to you and which worry you. It is equally important that they also feel able to tell your family things that trouble or worry them.

What's different? And what's the same?

We have already looked at some ways of helping to look after other children. What about children who are a little bit different from yourself? How do you see them?

For instance, children who are disabled also like to do the same things as any other child but may have a different way of doing it or may need some help. Even so, they still have fun joining in with other children and having friends like you!

That's why it is important to look at a child's "ability", that is, what a child can do, rather than the "disability", that is, what the child has difficulty doing, to make sure they get the same chances you have.

You may be helping to look after a disabled child for a short holiday break. Sometimes, a disabled child will not have any brothers or sisters so spending time with you will be fun for them. It will be like having a brother, a sister, or a new friend. Seeing a disabled child having lots of fun with you will make you feel good!

But it is not all fun and games ... helping look after a disabled child can also be very hard work and they may need lots of attention and help. And so it can be tiring for everybody.

There can also be other differences. The child who has come to stay might be from a different "ethnic background". This means that they will have a different skin colour to yourself, and their hair might be different. So, if you are white, and you have a black child coming to stay, he or she will have darker skin than yours and very dark hair. If you are black, and the child coming to stay with you is Chinese, he or she will have lighter skin than you and might have very straight hair.

Coming from a different ethnic background also means that these children will have come from families who might do things differently. They might speak another language at home. They might be used to eating food that is quite different to the food that you eat in your family. They may say their prayers differently and at different times. They might celebrate different festivals.

There will be a lot to find out, and a lot to learn!

Even though there might be these and other differences, there's more that's the same! You are all children who need to be properly looked after and have a nice time growing up!

What kinds of difficulties can disabled children have?

Some children who are disabled have a physical impairment. This means that they may have difficulties in walking or moving around in the way that you can. Because of this, some children may use a wheelchair, callipers or crutches to help them get around.

Look at the two pictures below. Can you see that the children still have shoes on the same as you do when you go out?

This is a photograph of me ready to go out

Try and think of other ways that you could move around the house without standing on your feet. Which ways can you think of?

_____

_____

_____

_____

Here's a little game to play!

Get a family member or friend to do this with you. Sit on a chair and pretend that you are sitting in a wheelchair. Then ask the person you are with to stand in front of you and speak to you for a few moments. How did this make you feel?

_____

_____

_____

Now, ask the person you are with to swap over with you, and you stand up and talk to them while they sit.

In the space below, write down what you both thought about this.

_____

_____

_____

_____

_____

Can you imagine how it must feel having to sit in a wheelchair all or most of the time and have people look down at you when they talk to you? It's not very nice, is it?

Take a minute to think about how we can talk to children and other people who use a wheelchair so that they feel as important as you. What about trying to make you an equal height to them? You can do this by getting another chair and sitting next to them. Or, what about bending down so you are still on the same level as them? Better still, if you are able, why not ask the person what makes them most comfortable when talking to other people?

But remember that, even if a child or adult uses a wheelchair, they still have feelings and like to feel good about themselves the same as you!

There are, of course, many other disabilities. Sometimes children may have health difficulties or may not be able see or hear properly or eat food the same way as you can.

Can you imagine what it must be like not to be able to hear your family's voices, or birds singing, or your favourite pop band or the TV?

Some children have a learning disability. This means that they have problems about learning and they may not be able to speak as well or to look after themselves as well as other children do. They may like your help to do ordinary things, even if they are older than you are.

Difficult times and what you can do

Do you remember earlier in the book when we looked at "talking works in lots of ways"? Well, sometimes, children who come to stay with you and your family may talk to you about things that are making them upset. In the space below, write down some of the things that a child has said to you and whom you spoke to about this.

_____

_____

_____

_____

_____

_____

_____

_____

_____

_____

_____

_____

_____

Date

_____

What children might do in your home

Here's some things that children sometimes do when living with a foster family. Because there are so many different things that children who visit you might do, or different ways in which they may behave, it would be impossible to cover everything in this section.

Here's one example. Sometimes, children who know how to use the toilet will mess themselves or wet themselves by accident. Sometimes they might do this on purpose. Sometimes they can't help it. Whatever the reason, this can be difficult to understand. It can also be extremely embarrassing, particularly if you are all out shopping at the time.

How you and your family deal with that child at that time will be important. By playing it "cool" and just helping them to get washed and changed into clean clothing will be the right way. This can be difficult when you might want to shout "ugh" or feel yourself being angry or upset.

Sometimes, it might look as if your parents and other adults in your family are letting other children get away with things that you would get told off for! This will seem very unfair so it will be important for you to talk about how you feel.

Let's have a look at some of the different kinds of behaviour and how this may make you feel. Talk to your family and social worker about these things so that they can help you to look at what you can do to make you feel better about this.

● **Sometimes children and young people will mess or wet themselves.**

This makes me feel

_____

_____

The reasons they might do this are because

_____

_____

To make myself feel better about this I will

_____

_____

● **Sometimes children living with you might hit you or another member of your family.**

This makes me feel

_____

_____

They might do this because

_____

_____

To make myself feel better about this I will

_____

_____

- **Sometimes they will bunk off school or be excluded, that is, told that they can't come to school any more.**

This makes me feel

_____

_____

The reasons they might do this are because

_____

_____

To make myself feel better about this I will

_____

_____

- **Sometimes children will hide food. They might make themselves sick while sitting at the dinner table. Their eating problems might make eating difficult for you.**

These things make me feel

_____

_____

The reasons they might do this are because

_____

_____

To make myself feel better about this I will

_____

_____

● Sometimes children and young people will say or shout hurtful things to you or other members of your family.

This makes me feel

_____

_____

The reasons they might do this are because

_____

_____

To make myself feel better about this I will

_____

_____

● Sometimes children and young people might try to touch parts of your body that are private

This makes me feel

_____

_____

The reasons they might do this are because

_____

_____

To make myself feel better about these things I will

_____

_____

- **Sometimes children or young people may ask you to touch parts of their body that are private, or ask you to touch another child.**

This makes me feel

_____

_____

The reasons they might do this are because

_____

_____

To make myself feel better about these things I will

_____

- **Sometimes children may break your things or hide them.**

This makes me feel

_____

_____

The reasons they might do this are because

_____

_____

To make myself feel better about these things I will

_____

No one will have all these behaviour problems and some children who come and stay may have none of them. All the children who come and stay in your home will also behave in ways that you like.

This page has been left free for you to write down other types of behaviour — good and bad — that you have seen in the children who have come to live with you. Don't forget to write down how this made you feel, whom you talked to about this, and, if it was bad behaviour, what you did to make yourself feel better.

_____

_____

_____

_____

_____

_____

_____

_____

_____

_____

_____

_____

_____

_____

_____

_____

Date
_____

If you feel upset or think that things are unfair

Have you ever felt like screaming or shouting? Have you ever felt so angry that you hated everyone including your own parents and other members of your family? Have you ever said or shouted things that you've later thought you should not have or wish you hadn't?

Well, here is your chance to write down all the things that make you cross about looking after other children.

Maybe it's because they seem to get more presents than you at Christmas or get more pocket money. Maybe it's because they've been taken out somewhere nice and you haven't. Maybe you've been at school all day and they have been doing other things. Or maybe it's because they have gone to bed later than you.

All of these things can seem unfair at times. And you may feel cross and upset.

In the spaces below and on the next page, write down some of the things that make you feel cross, upset or not treated fairly.

Write down whom you have talked to about these things and what you can do to make yourself heard.

Memories and keeping track

These next pages are for you to write something about the children who have stayed with you. You can use photographs and drawings to remember the children whom you have helped to look after. This will help you to remember all the children who came to stay with you and your family.

No matter what you use these pages for, don't forget to write down the names of the children in the photographs, the dates they came to stay with you, when they left, and something nice you did together.

At the end of this section, you will find a special space for you to write down any other thoughts or feelings about helping to foster other children.

Any other thoughts or feelings?

These next two pages are for you to write down anything else about your thoughts and feelings about helping to look after other children.

- _____
- _____
- _____
- _____

Date _____

- _____
- _____
- _____
- _____

Date _____

- _____
- _____
- _____
- _____

Date _____

- _____
- _____
- _____
- _____

Date _____

- _____
- _____
- _____
- _____

Date
_____

- _____
- _____
- _____
- _____

Date
_____

- _____
- _____
- _____
- _____

Date
_____

Remember!

You are and always will be very important to the other children you help to look after.

Most importantly, YOU are a very important part of your family. Your family cares for you and loves you.

So when you have feelings and thoughts that you want to share, don't forget that your family is always there for you.

Below is a list of some information materials, workbooks and short novels that might be of interest. This is not a comprehensive list, and there are many other materials out there! You can get your parents or social worker to help you look for these at www.amazon.co.uk.

Children's guides

Adoption: What it is and what it means

Shaila Shah, BAAF 2003
Available in English and Welsh
This booklet provides a good introduction to adoption and the surrounding issues for children and young people. Comprehensive information is presented in a colourful and vividly illustrated format.

Fostering: What it is and what it means

Shaila Shah, BAAF 2003
Covering how children come to be fostered, how the right family is found and information on care plans, school and contact, this accessible and jargon-free booklet provides a good introduction to fostering, the process and procedures.

What Happens in Court?

Hedi Argent and Mary Lane, BAAF 2003
This publication will help young readers to understand the role a court could play in their lives. Who's who in court, what happens there and the various court orders are discussed in a manner suitable for young people in foster care or going to be adopted.

Workbooks to use with children

My Life and Me

Jean Camis, BAAF 2001
A comprehensive life story workbook which will help children living apart from their family of origin record memories of their past and birth family.

Family Talk

Celia Macliver and Maureen Thom, BAAF 1990
This picture pack for use with children aged 6-11 is designed to help them talk about family life and understand the implications of a brother or sister joining their family.

Talking Pictures

Philip King, BAAF 1989
Containing three sets of picture sheets and guidelines for use, this picture pack is a practical tool to aid social workers in communicating with children.

All of the above titles are available from BAAF,
Skyline House, 200 Union Street, London SE1 0LX
www.baaf.org.uk

Books by Jacqueline Wilson

Jacqueline Wilson has written several books for teenagers. Some relevant titles include:

Dustbin Baby

Corgi, 2002
April was left in a rubbish bin when only a few hours old, and has spent her life in foster homes. As she enters her teens, she decides to try and find her birth family.

The Story of Tracy Beaker

Corgi, 1991
Tracy Beaker lives in a foster home and dreams about finding a "forever family". When writing her life story she meets Cam, a writer who comes to visit the home.

The Suitcase Kid

Corgi, 1993
Andrea's parents have recently divorced, leaving her shuttling between two different families. This book explores her attempt to come to terms with her new way of life.

Available from all good libraries and bookshops

This Certificate
of achievement is awarded to

_____

for completing this book

We are fostering

and for all the help and support

you have given to other children

_____

SIGNED

_____

SOCIAL WORKER FOR